THE MUSIC OF
GEORGE GERSHWIN
FOR CLARINET
Arranged by Robin de Smet

Wise Publications
London/New York/Sydney

Exclusive Distributors:
Music Sales Limited,
8/9 Frith Street, London W1V 5TZ, England.
Music Sales Pty. Limited,
120 Rothschild Avenue, Rosebery, NSW 2018, Australia.

This book © Copyright 1987 by Wise Publications.
ISBN 0.7119.1332.3
Order No. AM 68495

Designed by Pearce Marchbank Studio.

Compiled and arranged by Robin De Smet.

Music Sales complete catalogue lists thousands of titles and is free from
your local music book shop, or direct from Music Sales Limited.
Please send a cheque or postal order for £1.50 for postage to
Music Sales Limited, 8/9 Frith Street, London W1V 5TZ.

Printed in England by
Halstan & Co. Limited, Amersham, Bucks.

Bess, You Is My Woman

Music by George Gershwin

But Not For Me

Music by George Gershwin

Embraceable You

Music by George Gershwin

Fascinating Rhythm

Music by George Gershwin

An American In Paris

Music by George Gershwin

A Foggy Day

Music by George Gershwin

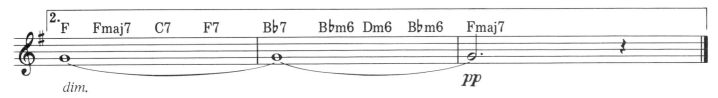

How Long Has This Been Going On?

Music by George Gershwin

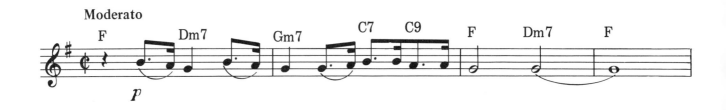

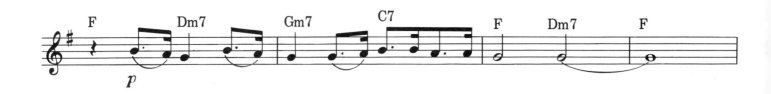

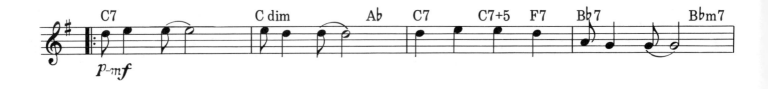

I Got Plenty O' Nuttin'

Music by George Gershwin

I Got Rhythm

Music by George Gershwin

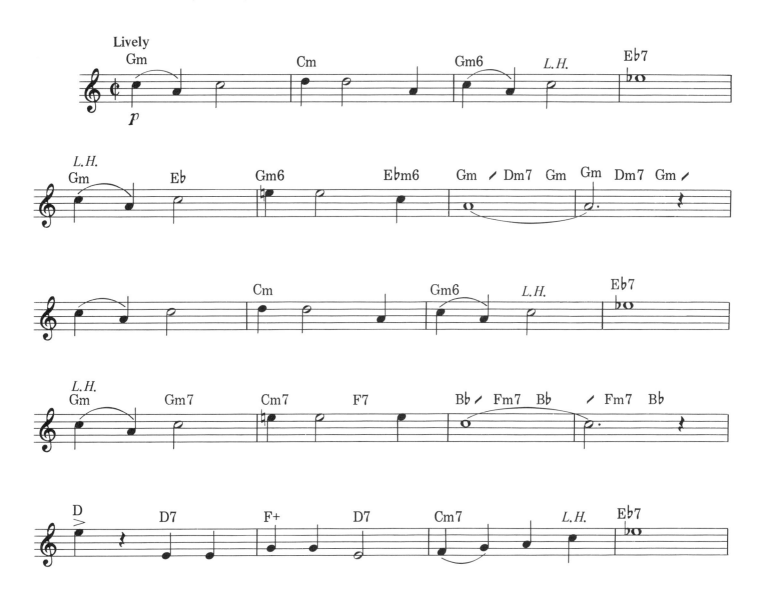

Rhapsody In Blue

Composed by George Gershwin

I'll Build A Stairway To Paradise

Music by George Gershwin

It Ain't Necessarily So

Music by George Gershwin

Let's Call The Whole Thing Off

Music by George Gershwin

The Man I Love

Music by George Gershwin

Nice Work If You Can Get It

Music by George Gershwin

Oh, Lady Be Good

Music by George Gershwin

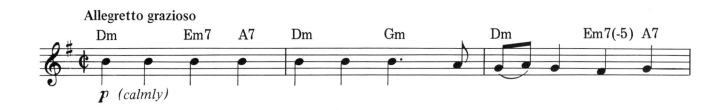

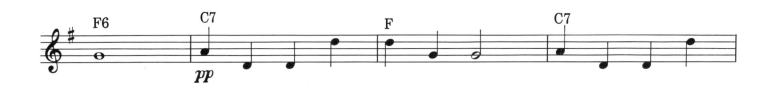

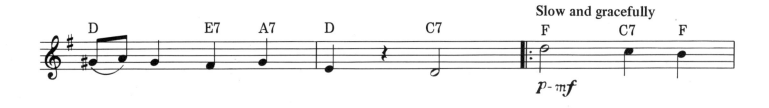

Somebody Loves Me

Music by George Gershwin

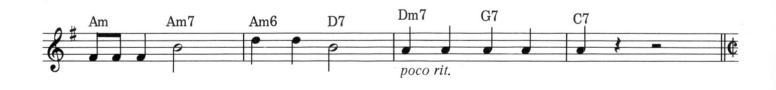

Someone To Watch Over Me

Music by George Gershwin

Strike Up The Band

Music by George Gershwin

Swanee

Music by George Gershwin

's Wonderful

Music by George Gershwin

They All Laughed

Music by George Gershwin

They Can't Take That Away From Me

Music by George Gershwin

Summertime

Music by George Gershwin

The Beatles

Enya

Phil Collins

Van Morrison

Bob Dylan

Sting

Paul Simon

Tracy Chapman

Eric Clapton

Pink Floyd

New Kids On The Block

Bryan Adams

Tina Turner

Elton John

Bee Gees

Whitney Houston

AC/DC

Bringing you the words

All the latest in rock and pop. Plus the brightest and best in West End show scores. Music books for every instrument under the sun. And exciting new teach-yourself ideas like "Let's Play Keyboard" - in cassette/book packs, or on video. Available from all good music shops.

and music

Music Sales' complete catalogue lists thousands of titles and is available free from your local music shop, or direct from Music Sales Limited. Please send a cheque or postal order for £1.50 (for postage) to:

Music Sales Limited
Newmarket Road,
Bury St Edmunds,
Suffolk IP33 3YB

Buddy

Five Guys Named Moe

Les Misérables

West Side Story

Phantom Of The Opera

Show Boat

The Rocky Horror Show

Bringing you the world's best music.